MUSIC OF TODAY

Arranged by
JOHN BRIMHALL

Songs From Walt Disney's

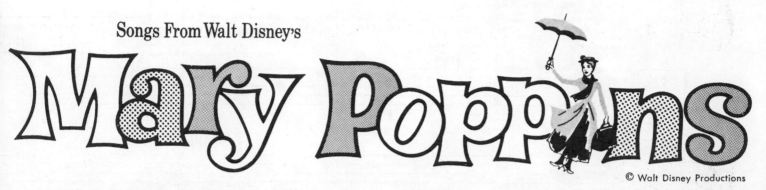

© Walt Disney Productions

Music and Lyrics by RICHARD M. SHERMAN and ROBERT B. SHERMAN

Contents

©1963 and 1965 by WONDERLAND MUSIC COMPANY

HANSEN
PUBLICATIONS INC.

From Walt Disney's "MARY POPPINS"

A SPOONFUL OF SUGAR

By
RICHARD M. SHERMAN
and ROBERT B. SHERMAN

CHORUS

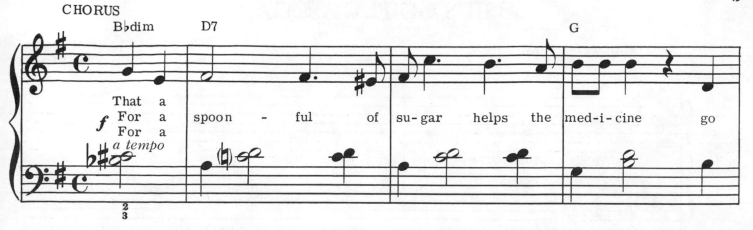

That a
For a spoon - ful of su - gar helps the med-i-cine go
For a

down, The med-i-cine go dow - wown, med-i-cine go down. Just a

spoon - ful of sug-ar helps the med-i-cine go down

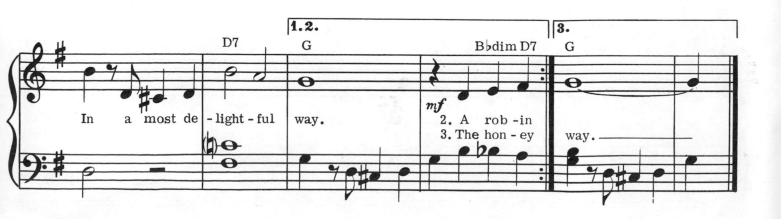

In a most de -light-ful way.
2. A rob -in
3. The hon -ey way.

4

From Walt Disney's "MARY POPPINS"

LET'S GO FLY A KITE

By
RICHARD M. SHERMAN
and ROBERT B. SHERMAN

Moderately Fast
VERSE

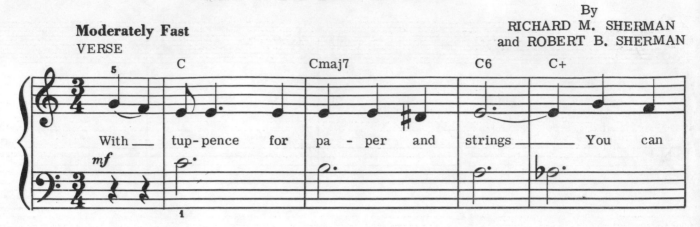

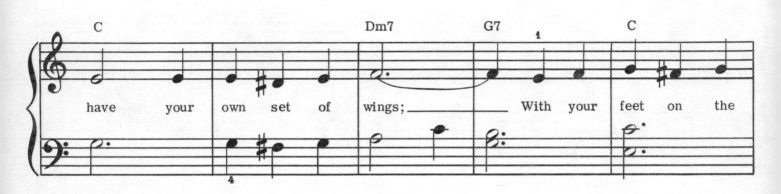

CHORUS

From Walt Disney's "MARY POPPINS"

JOLLY HOLIDAY

By
RICHARD M. SHERMAN
and ROBERT B. SHERMAN

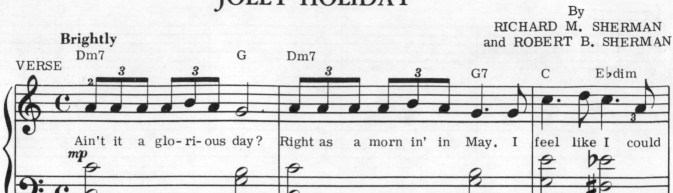

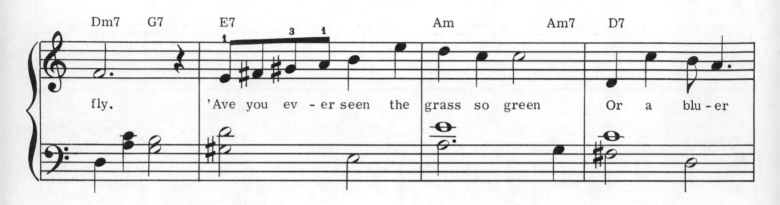

From Walt Disney's "MARY POPPINS"

CHIM CHIM CHER-EE

By
RICHARD M. SHERMAN
and ROBERT B. SHERMAN

blow me a kiss and that's luck - y too.
roof tops of Lon - don, coo, what a sight!
Chim chim-in-ey Chim Chim Cher - ee, chim cher - oo!

VERSE

Now, as the lad - der of life 'as been strung, You may think a
I choose me bris - tles with pride, yes, I do, A broom for the

sweep's on the bot - tom - most rung. Though I spends me time in the
shaft and a brush for the flue. Though Im cov - ered with soot from me

2nd time D. S. al Fine

ash - es and smoke, In this 'ole wide world there's no 'ap - pi - er bloke.
'ead to me toes, A sweep knows 'e's wel - come wher - ev - er 'e goes.

From Walt Disney's "MARY POPPINS"

STEP IN TIME
(THE CHIMMEY SWEEP DANCE)

By
RICHARD M. SHERMAN
and ROBERT B. SHERMAN

Spirited

Kick your knees up, step in time! Kick your knees up,
Spin a-bout and step in time! Spin a-bout and

step in time! Nev-er need a rea-son, nev-er need a rhyme,
step in time! Nev-er need a rea-son, nev-er need a rhyme,

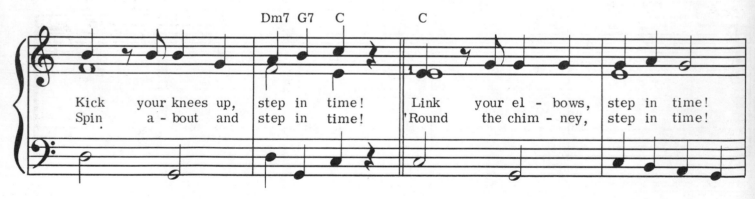

Kick your knees up, step in time! Link your el-bows, step in time!
Spin a-bout and step in time! 'Round the chim-ney, step in time!

Link your el-bows, step in time! Nev-er need a rea-son,
'Round the chim-ney, step in time! Nev-er need a rea-son,

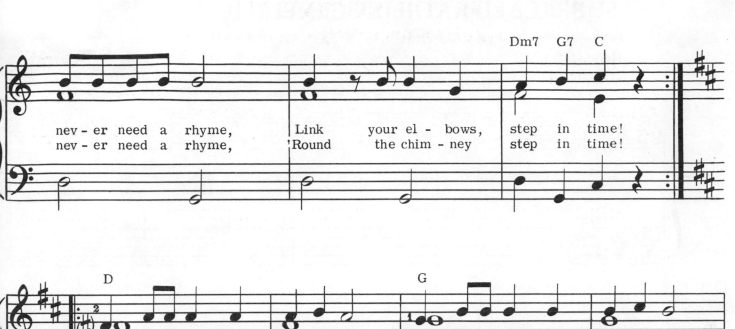

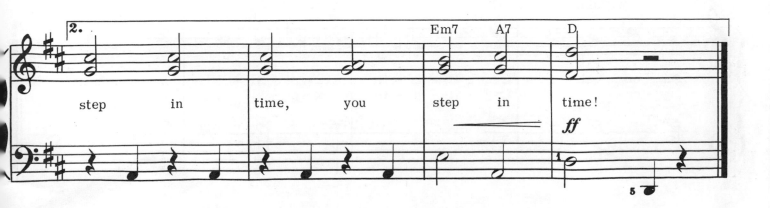

From Walt Disney's "MARY POPPINS:

SUPERCALIFRAGILISTICEXPIALIDOCIOUS

(SUPER-CALI-FRAGIL-ISTIC-EXPI-ALI-DOCIOUS)

By
RICHARD M. SHERMAN
and ROBERT B. SHERMAN

Brightly
CHORUS

1.2.3. Sup - er - cal - i - frag - il - is - tic - ex - pi - al - i - do - cious!
4. Sup - er - cal - i - frag - il - is - tic - ex - pi - al - i - do - cious!

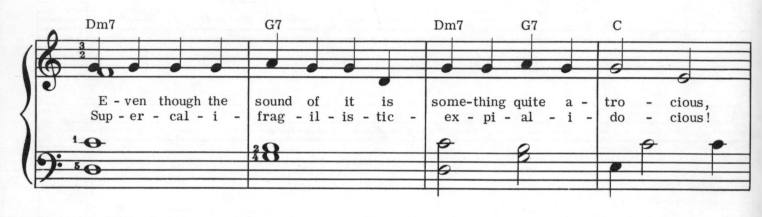

E - ven though the sound of it is some-thing quite a - tro - cious,
Sup - er - cal - i - frag - il - is - tic - ex - pi - al - i - do - cious!

If you say it loud e - nough you'll al - ways sound pre - co - cious,
Sup - er - cal - i - frag - il - is - tic - ex - pi - al - i - do - cious!

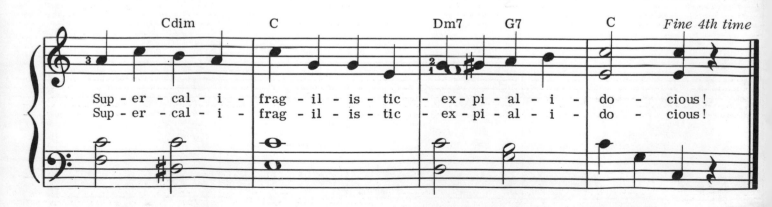

Sup - er - cal - i - frag - il - is - tic - ex - pi - al - i - do - cious!
Sup - er - cal - i - frag - il - is - tic - ex - pi - al - i - do - cious!

Fine 4th time

From Walt Disney's "MARY POPPINS"

STAY AWAKE

By
RICHARD M. SHERMAN
and ROBERT B. SHERMAN

Slowly and Tenderly

From Walt Disney's "MARY POPPINS"

FEED THE BIRDS
(TUPPENCE A BAG)

By
RICHARD M. SHERMAN
and ROBERT B. SHERMAN

Slow, with feeling

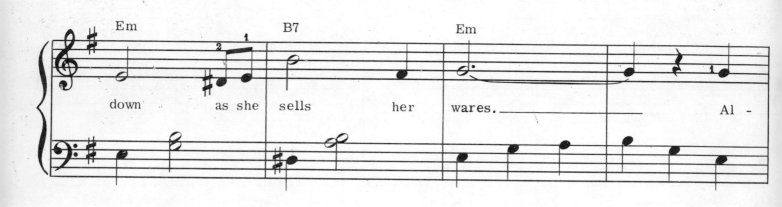

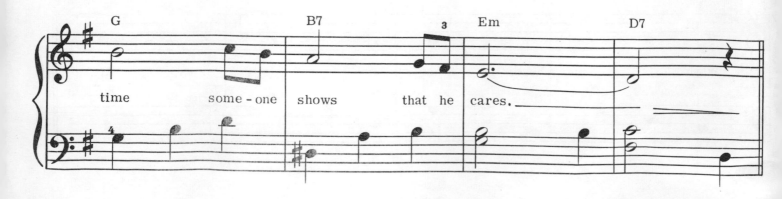